A DAY IN THE JUNGLE

By Pat Patterson
Illustrated by Olena Kassian

Consultant, Dr. Judith Eger, Dept. of Mammalogy, Royal Ontario Museum

 An OWL Magazine/Golden Press Book

©1985 by Pat Patterson. Illustrations ©1985 by Olena Kassian. All rights reserved. Printed in the U.S.A. by Western Publishing Company, Inc. OWL Magazine is a trademark of the Young Naturalist Foundation. GOLDEN®, GOLDEN & DESIGN®, GOLDEN PRESS®, and A LITTLE GOLDEN BOOK® are trademarks of Western Publishing Company, Inc. Library of Congress Catalog Card Number: 85-70826, Canadian ISBN 0-920775-03-9 U.S. ISBN 0-307-02028-2/ISBN 0-307-60286-9 (lib. bdg.)

F G H I J

Published in Canada by Greey de Pencier Books, Toronto. Canadian Cataloguing in Publication Data Patterson, Pat. A day in the jungle ISBN 0-920775-03-9 I. Kassian, Olena. II. Title. PS8581.A77D39 1985   jC813'.54   C85-098291-X PZ10.3.P37Da 1985

It was a hot afternoon in an African jungle.
Silkie, a young Colobus monkey, sat in a
mahogany tree. He was thinking about exploring
the jungle on his own.

Silkie was six months old, quite old enough
to have an adventure. Before he left on his
journey, Silkie's mother combed his silky fur with
her fingers.

Silkie's mother had given him many lessons in tree travel, so he knew how to swing from branch to branch. He started on the lower branches and went carefully at first.

As he passed by, Silkie saw a sunbird hovering by a flower. It was eating tiny insects and sipping sweet nectar.

Farther on, Silkie was about to jump down onto the ground. But he saw something that made him stay where he was.

It was a royal python, a snake that kills other animals by coiling around them and squeezing. Silkie thought that he didn't want that kind of hug.

Silkie nearly lost his balance when the snake slithered up the tree after him. But before it reached him, he leaped to another tree.

He hung by one arm, watching the python
flick its tongue in and out of its mouth.

Silkie left the snake behind and settled in a tree with sweet fruit and juicy leaves. He was hungry, and these were his favorite foods. When he picked a nice, ripe ackee he discovered that a longlegged insect had gotten there first.

After lunch, Silkie climbed down from the tree
to look at a pond. A bird called a lilytrotter trotted
across the pond on a path made of big water
lily leaves.

The pond led into a river, and Silkie saw
something large and frightening swimming
across it. It was a leopard. Silkie knew that
leopards are fast-moving and can even climb
trees quickly.

And he knew that leopards like to eat monkeys!
Silkie was terrified, until he realized that the
leopard could not smell him because the wind was
blowing Silkie's scent away.

A moment later, Silkie saw feathers flying.
The leopard had probably caught a big bird. Silkie
climbed further up into the trees and swung away.

Later, Silkie saw a family of huge gorillas coming toward him. He was so nervous that he dropped a fruit. It crashed through the branches and startled the biggest gorilla.

The big gorilla drummed angrily on his chest
and barked. Then he roared loudly at Silkie.

Poor Silkie! Was he going to be eaten, after all?
No, he wasn't. Gorillas eat fruit and vegetables,
not monkeys.

Silkie could see the gorilla family through the trees. They had made sleeping nests out of leaves and twigs — all except the huge male. He was too heavy to climb, so he sat on a pile of leaves on the ground. Soon the gorillas were all sound asleep.

It was beginning to get dark, and Silkie was tired. Just before he closed his eyes, a beautiful moth fluttered past.

Down below him, a mother elephant checked to make sure her sleeping baby was safe.

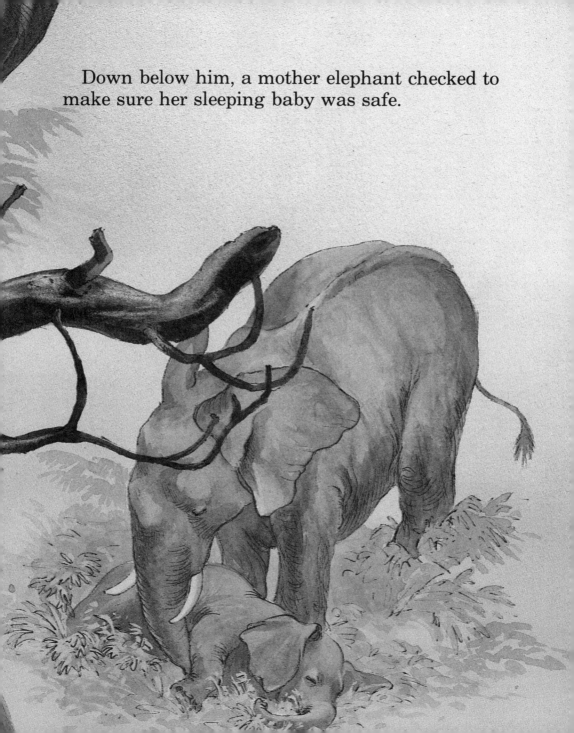

When Silkie woke in the morning, the gorillas and the elephants were gone. The only creature he could see was a chameleon enjoying a breakfast of insects.

Silkie was hungry, and food reminded him of
home. Off he went through the treetops to find his
mother.

His mother was happy that Silkie had enjoyed his first jungle adventure, all on his own. Sometime soon, he would be ready to live on his own all the time. But, for now, he was glad to be home.